Language Through Music

Book 2

An essential companion for early learning
and the teaching of English
as a foreign language

by Caroline and Ben Lumsden

family and home face and body monsters colthes food zoo animals

EDITION PETERS

London · Frankfurt · Leipzig · New York

For Anna and Juliette Leader

Peters Edition Limited
10–12 Baches Street
London
N1 6DN

Tel: 020 7553 4000
Fax: 020 7490 4921
e-mail: sales@uk.edition-peters.com
Internet: www.edition-peters.com

First published 2002
© 2002 by Hinrichsen Edition, Peters Edition Limited, London

ISBN 1 901507 96 3

A catalogue record for this book is available from the British Library

Music-setting by Andrew Jones

Cover and CD design and concept: www.adamhaystudio.com
Original artwork by Kate Hawley

Printed in Great Britain by Caligraving Limited
Thetford, Norfolk

Foreword

Language Through Music is a series of song books for teachers, group leaders, parents and grandparents. The books have been written specifically for those teaching students of English as a foreign language as well as children at foundation stage and key stages 1 and 2. In our household, the songs are sung and enjoyed by three-year-olds to ninety-three-year-olds!

Three books cover basic commands, actions, questions and answers through the following topics:

Book 1: Names   Actions   Numbers   The Alphabet   Objects   Colour   Pets and Farm Animals
Book 2: Family and Home   Face and Body   Monsters   Clothes   Food   Zoo Animals
Book 3: School   Days and Dates   Birthday   Party Games   Work and Play   Time and Timetables

All the songs can be sung without accompaniment and can be learnt easily by playing copycat. Children do enjoy live accompaniments, however, so simple piano parts and guitar chords are provided for those lucky enough to have players to hand. The companion CD's provide further options, both for learning the songs and for lively backing in performance.

We have included as many ideas and suggestions as possible to create a compact and portable reference library. All the songs and actions should be used to stimulate ideas from the children and for creative activities. Around the edges of the text pages are suggestions of words or actions that you can make into flash cards as extra resource material.

All the related activities for each song have been graded with a star system:

*easily managed   **moderately difficult   ***more difficult.

This is useful if you want to reinforce a particular teaching point by returning to a familiar song with a new, more difficult game, or to adapt the different levels for different age groups.

We would like to record our gratitude to all the children who have worked on the songs with us in France and England. In France, thanks go to Madame Fontaine and the children of École Jean Bouchet, Beaugeay and Marie Christine and the children of École Champlain, Brouage, Charente Maritime; in England, Glyn Oxley, Rebecca Peacock, Kirsten Schofield, Heather Graham and Janet Kerr, and the children of Beauchamp Music Group, Churcham, Gloucestershire. Special thanks go to William, Christopher, Bethan, Sophie, Madeline, Friederike, Rosie, Rosemary, Heather, Sophie, Georgina and Annabelle for their contribution to the CD, and to Kirsten Graham of Horfield Primary School, Westbury on Trym, Bristol, who acted as consultant and provided percussion ideas for the project.

Caroline and Ben Lumsden

Guitar chords to accompany the songs

Major chords

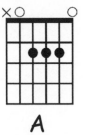 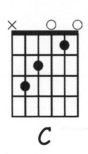 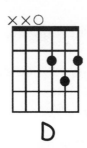 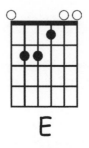 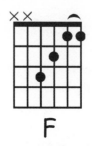 

A   C   D   E   F   G

Seventh chords

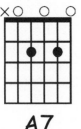 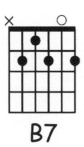 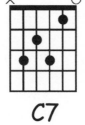 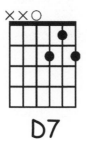 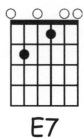 

A7   B7   C7   D7   E7   G7

Minor chords

Minor seventh chord

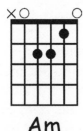  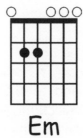 

Am   Bm   Dm   Em   Fm   Am7

Contents

6

 1-2

Hello everybody

2. *Leader:* Hello ev'rybody
   All: Hello ev'rybody
   Leader: What is your name?
   All: What is your name?

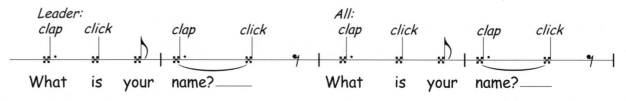

3rd person:
My name's Friederike.
4th person:
My name is William.
3rd person:
Very pleased to meet you.
4th person:
Very pleased to meet you.

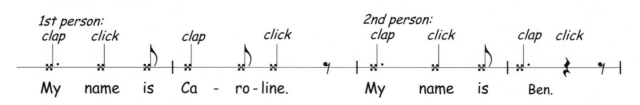

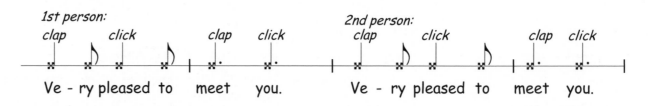

Leader: Let's start again.
All: Let's start again.

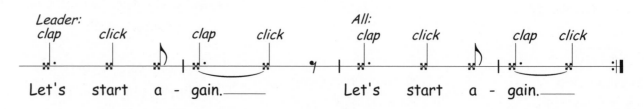

Hello   Salut   Jonapot   Guten Tag   Dav   Konichiwa   Hallo   Buon Giorno   Ahlan   Namaste

Dobry   Dzien   Dias   Buenos   kal   Hosca   Bonjour

Ya sas   Ola   Molo   Shalom   Goede   More   Szia

Very pleased to meet you!

*Copy cat
Say a phrase
at a time.
Everyone copies.

*Change character
Change emphasis
on the word *"hello"*
sometimes accenting
"hel-" and sometimes *"-lo"*.

*Two groups
Divide into two groups.
One group copies the
other. One person from
each half comes to the
front to say their name
and to shake hands.

*Change voice
Vary your tone of voice
– high, low, loud, soft.

*Tap, clap, click or slap
Keep a beat
going while saying
"Hello everybody ..."

**Walk in line
Form two lines facing each other.
The second line copies the first line.
The top two people say their names,
walk toward each other, shake hands
and then walk down the middle of the
others so that a new top couple do
the actions. Then it is the next
couple's turn and so on.

**Lead the circle
When confident enough, one
person leads and sings from
the middle of a circle, turning
round while deciding which
person to shake hands with.

**Who is this?
Tap someone on the shoulder
and ask *"Who is this?"*
Everyone replies with
the name. Change leaders.

***Hello, around the world
Ask if anyone
knows the word for
"hello" in another language
as well as their own and
add them to the list
round this page.

Dobry den   Goeie More   Chao   Zdravstvuitye   Sala maleikum   Wai   Kali mera

How many sisters?

3-6

2. How many brothers?
3. How many pets?

I have one!

*How many sisters?
Ask everyone in turn,
" How many sisters do you
have, 3, 2, 1 or none ?"
(Hold up fingers when asking)
Reply:"I have ..."

*How many brothers?
As above, but ask about
brothers instead.

*Everyone sings
Everyone sings
How many sisters
and the chosen person
replies *"I have ..."*
Repeat as many times
as is necessary for
everyone to
have a go.

**Sing and weave
Everyone sings
in a circle while one
person weaves in and out.
When the song finishes,
he/she places his/her hand on
the shoulders of the nearest
person (from behind).
That person says *"I have ..."*
and becomes the new
weaver. And so on.

**Sing and circle
Hold hands in a circle.
Choose one person to be in the
middle. Circle left while singing
How many sisters? The person in
the middle replies. Repeat with a
new person in the middle.
This time circle right.

**How many pets?
Do exactly the same
as *How many sisters*,
but ask *"How many pets?"*
instead. Reply: *"I have ..."*

***Change leader
Choose someone to be
the leader to ask or sing
*"How many sisters/brothers
do you have?"*

***Everyone weave
As *Sing and weave*
but the first person
chosen follows the new
person chosen, weaving
in and out. Go on adding
a new leader so that
you end up with a
long train.

Draw your family tree!

7–10

Capo: 4th fret

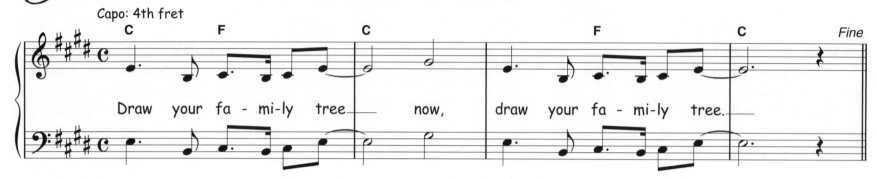

Draw your fa - mi-ly tree___ now, draw your fa - mi-ly tree.___

Name your mo-ther's mo-ther here,___ whom she mar-ried and___ the year.___

*Sing

Sing *Draw your family tree* while holding up and pointing to Tom's family tree on page 11.

**Draw your family tree

Ask everyone to draw their own family tree.

2. Name your father's father here.
   Whom he married and the year.
3. Name your mother's father too,
   Uncles, aunts and cousins new...
4. Name your brothers, sisters too,
   All the family close to you.

**In pairs

Using the family tree ask,
"How many brothers does Tom have?"

Reply: *"He has one."*

***How many do you have?

Ask, *"How many aunts do you have?"*
Reply: *"I have two."*
or *"I haven't any."*

Tom's family tree

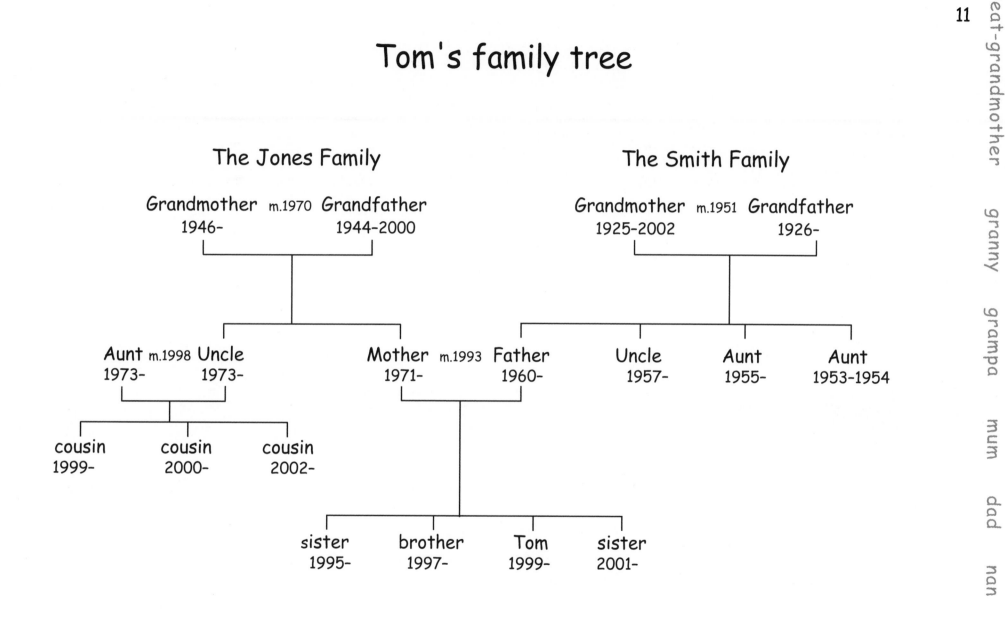

The Jones Family

Grandmother m.1970 Grandfather
1946–   1944–2000

The Smith Family

Grandmother m.1951 Grandfather
1925–2002   1926–

Aunt m.1998 Uncle
1973–   1973–

Mother m.1993 Father
1971–   1960–

Uncle
1957–

Aunt
1955–

Aunt
1953–1954

cousin
1999–

cousin
2000–

cousin
2002–

sister
1995–

brother
1997–

Tom
1999–

sister
2001–

Number 23

Leader: Who lives in your house, in your house, in your house?
Who lives in your house, at number twenty-three?

1st person: ".. and me."

Everyone: That's who lives in your house, at number twenty-three!

Five people and six animals live in my house.   Four people and three animals live in mine.

13

Who lives in your house?

*Listen and sing
Play or sing
Number 23. On the
second time through
everyone begins
to join in.

**Who lives in your house?
Ask each person in turn
the names of the people and
animals who live in their house.
Reply: *"In my house there is ..."*

***Where do you live?
Leader: *"Where do you live?"*
Reply: *"I live in ...
It is a big/small
village/town."*
Change leaders.

*Draw your house
Ask everyone to draw
their own house and put the
people that live there
at the windows.

**Sing the names
Sing the second verse of
Number 23. Choose someone to
sing the names of the people who
live in their house, ending with
"... and me." Everyone sings
the last line.

***Do you live in a house?
Ask: *"Do you live in a house?"*
Reply: *"Yes, I do* or
*No, I live ...
(... in an apartment ...
... in a caravan ...
... on a boat etc.)"*
Change leaders.

**How many?
Ask everyone to
write down the names
of the people and animals
living in their house.

**Change leaders
As above, but a new leader
sings the question. Everyone
joins in the last line.

***Town or country?
Leader: *"Do you live in the town?"*
Reply: *"Yes I do"* or *"No, I live
in the country."*
Change leaders.

I live in a village   I live in the country   I live in a small flat   I live in

I live in a big house   I live in a town   I live on a farm

In my house there is mummy, daddy, granny, my brother, 2 cats, a dog, 6 rabbits and me.

earings

eye brows

eyelashes

nostril

forehead

sunglasses

cap

hat

blue eyes

brown eyes

beard

glasses

moustache

Draw your face

*Rogues gallery
Ask everyone to draw
their own face for a
wall display.

*Touch your nose!
Touch different parts
of your face and say,
"Touch your eye ..." etc.
Everyone copies.
Change leader.

*Draw an eye
Everyone draws
a different part of the
face to be mounted and
used as flash cards.

*Flash and say
Hold up a flash
card of a nose and say,
"What is this?"
Reply: "It is a nose."
Change leaders.

**Two teams
Divide into two teams.
Give each team a dice.
Each team throws their
dice in turn. The first to get a 6
draws the outline of a face on
the board. Next throw a 5 for
each eye, a 4 for the nose, 3 for
the mouth, 2 for each ear and 1
for the hair.

*Touch and sing!
Sing Touch your elbow.
Everyone joins in with the actions.
Stretch on "reach for the sky",
crouch for "bend very low"
and curl up for
"keep very still and quiet."

*Touch and sing 2
As above but everyone
joins in the singing
as well as doing
the actions.

**Divide in two
Divide into two groups.
Each group takes it in
turns to sing an action.
Everyone sings the last phrase.

Touch your elbow

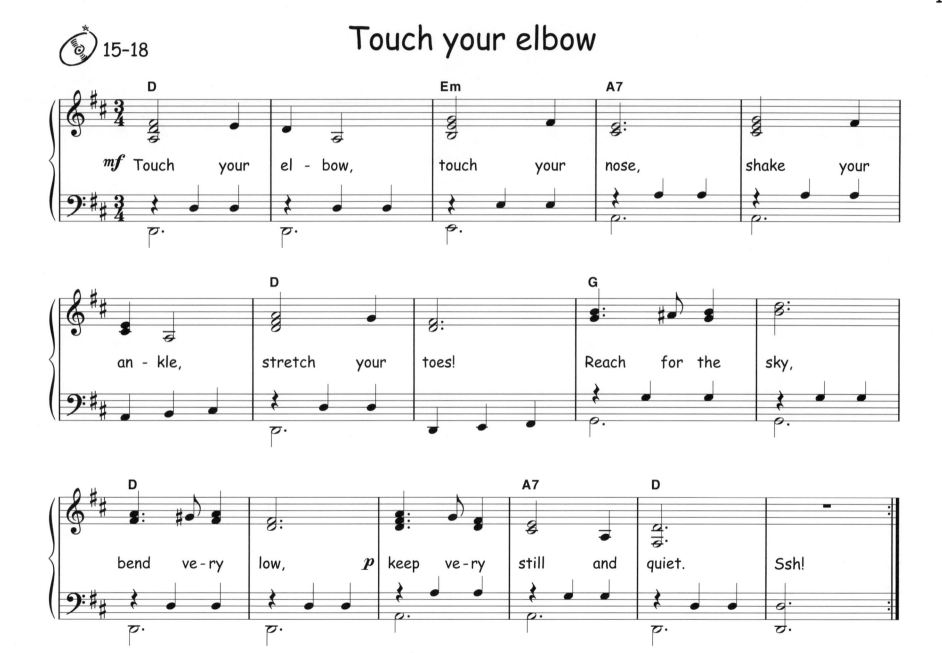

16

19-22

I have a mouth and nose

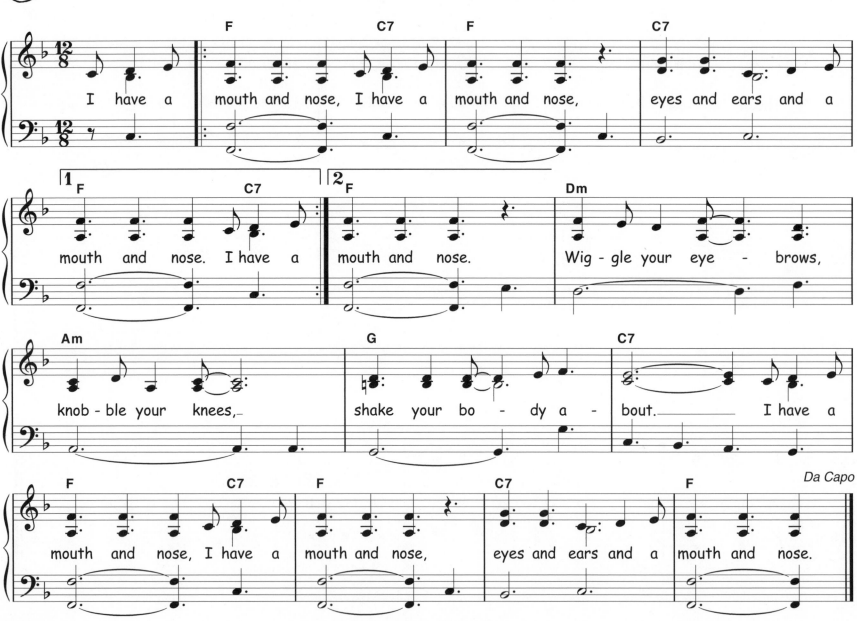

... point to ...

1. I have a mouth and nose, I have a mouth and nose, eyes and ears and a mouth and nose.
   I have a mouth and nose, I have a mouth and nose, eyes and ears and a mouth and nose.
   Wiggle your eyebrows, knobble your knees, shake your body about.
   I have a mouth and nose, I have a mouth and nose, eyes and ears and a mouth and nose.

2. I have some hair and teeth, I have some hair and teeth, cheeks and forehead and hair and teeth.
   Wiggle your eyebrows, knobble your knees, shake your body about.
   I have some hair and teeth, I have some hair and teeth, cheeks and forehead and hair and teeth.

3. I have two arms and legs, I have two arms and legs, elbows, knees and two arms and legs.
   Wiggle your eyebrows, knobble your knees, shake your body about.
   I have two arms and legs, I have two arms and legs, elbows, knees and two arms and legs.

4. I have two hands and feet, I have two hands and feet, fingers, toes and two hands and feet.
   Wiggle your eyebrows, knobble your knees, shake your body about.
   I have two hands and feet, I have two hands and feet, fingers, toes and two hands and feet.

*Sing
Sing *I have a mouth and nose,*
pointing to parts of the face.
Everyone copies.

*Point and say
Point to parts of the face
and say,"*What is this?*"
Reply: "*Your nose!*"

**Is this my nose?
Point to your mouth
and say,"*Is this my nose?*"
Reply: "*No, it's your mouth!*"

***Long or short
Ask,"*Do you have long
or short hair?*"
Reply: "*I have ...*"

Heads, bodies, legs

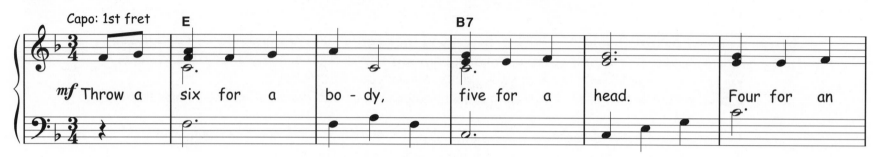

Capo: 1st fret

mf Throw a six for a bo - dy, five for a head. Four for an

arm and three for a leg. Two for the face and

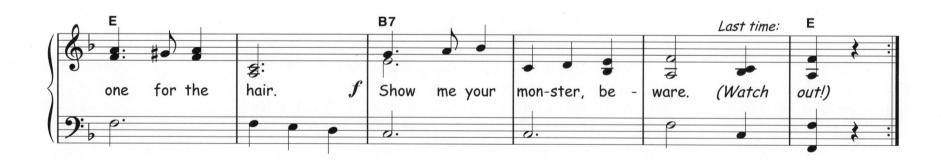

one for the hair. *f* Show me your mon-ster, be - ware. (Watch out!)

Last time:

Parts of the body

*Sing and point
Sing *Heads, bodies and legs,* holding up fingers for the numbers and pointing to the relevant parts of the body. Everyone copies.

*Sing, throw and draw
Sit in a circle to sing *Heads, bodies and legs.* While singing, the leader throws or rolls a large dice to someone who then throws it back ... and so on. The first person to get a 6 runs to the board and draws a body (just the shape, no body parts). When a 5 is thrown, that person runs to draw a head (just the shape, no features). Two 4's are needed for the arms, two 3's for the legs, a 2 for the face and a 1 for the hair.

**Make body parts
Paint and cut out huge body parts to use to build a 'monster' or 'creature' while singing *Heads, bodies and legs.*

**Sing, throw and build
As *Sing, throw and draw* but this time use flash cards to build your monster.

**Two teams
As *Sing, throw and draw* but this time have two dice and divide the group into two teams.

**Draw an animal
As *Sing, throw and draw* but change the word 'monster' in the song to 'creature' so that an animal can be drawn instead. Throw a 1 for the tail.

**What is this?
Ask,"*What is this?*", while pointing to your leg. Reply: "*That is your leg.*" Change leaders after every three times.

***Make a jigsaw
Ask everyone to draw a person or animal. Back it onto card and then cut up the various parts of the body. Exchange jigsaws. (Make sure that the back of each part has the person's name on it.)

chin shoulder

breasts jaw

waist chest

knee eyes

front ears

back nose

ribs neck

hips elbow

mouth lips tongue cheek nostrils eyelids eyebrows eyelashes forehead hair

Monster stomp

2. To do the monster stomp you have to swing your arms, swing your arms, swing your arms.
   To do the monster stomp you have to swing your arms, stop for the monster stomp.

3. To do the monster stomp you have to roll your head, roll your head, roll your head.
   To do the monster stomp you have to roll your head, stop for the monster stomp.

4. To do the monster stomp you have to do all three, do all three, do all three.
   To do the monster stomp you have to do all three, stop for the monster stomp. Aargh!

Make a monster

*Sing the song

Sing *Monster stomp*
doing all the actions.
Everyone joins in pulling a
horrible face on the
final *"Aargh!"*

**Draw a monster

Ask everyone to draw a monster.
Give out cards listing six
unusual features such as:
big, blue nose
six, small eyes
a huge mouth
long, green hair
four, fat arms
seven, tiny legs

**Ask questions

Ask questions
about the monsters.
"Is it big?" or
"Is it fat?"
Reply: *"No, it's
small and thin."*

**Make a monster puppet

Use any materials at hand to
make monster puppets, from old
socks and materials to bits of
dowling and foam balls, etc. Be as
inventive as possible. Use the
puppets for conversation.

***Describe your monster

Say
*"Tell me three things
about your monster."*
Reply: *"My monster has
(three legs,
long blue hair and
seven eyes!)."*

**Do this!

Ask someone with a puppet
to do various actions such as:
"open the door",
"close the desk,"
"stand up, sit down" etc.
Change leaders.

***Puppet conversation 1

Puppet 1: *"Hello!"*
Puppet 2: *"Hello! What's
your name?"*
Puppet 1: (*"Zacky"*)
Puppet 2: *"Hello (Zacky),
I'm (Patch!)"*
Puppet 1: *"Hello (Patch!)
Good to meet you."*
Puppet 2: *"Good to meet you too."*
Puppet 1: *"I like your (hair)."*
Puppet 2: *"Thank you."*

***Puppet conversation 2

Puppet 1: *"How are you?"*
Puppet 2: *"Very well, thanks!"*
Puppet 1: *"How many eyes
Do you have?"*
Puppet 2: *"I have six eyes."*
Puppet 1: *"What colour are they?"*
Puppet 2: *"They are blue, brown
and purple!"*
Puppet 1: *"(Wow!) Mine are pink!"*

Take the hat

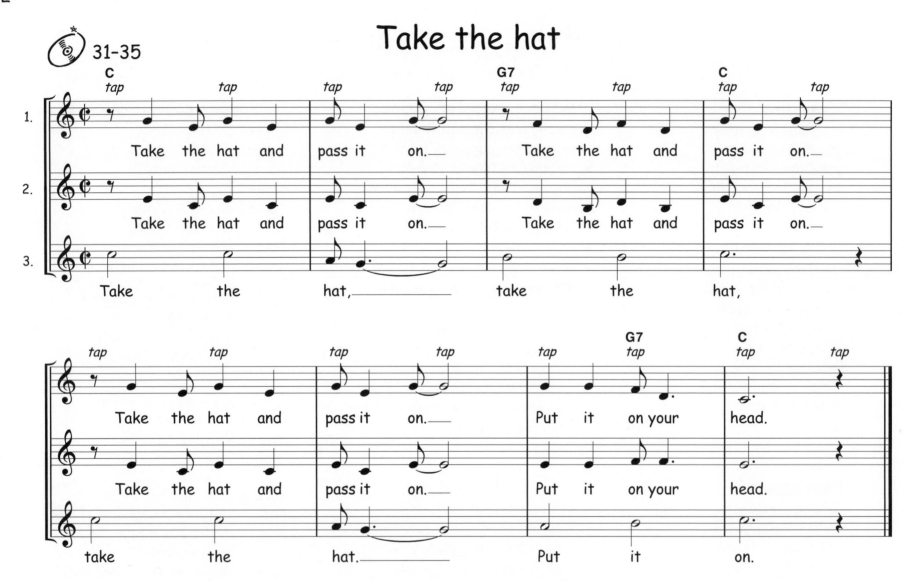

2. Take the shoe and pass it on. Put it on your foot.

3. Take the glove and pass it on. Put it on your hand.

4. Take the scarf and pass it on. Put it round your neck.

hat shoe glove scarf cap coat jacket jumper dress trousers trainers

Put it on!

***Listen and tap**
Listen to *Take the hat.*
Tap the beat, keeping a steady rhythm.

***Sing a line at a time**
The leader sings a line at a time. Everyone copies before singing all three lines, one after the other.

****Add the hat**
Sit in a circle.
While singing *Take the hat,* pass a hat around the circle on the beat. When the word 'head' is reached, the person receiving the hat puts it on his/her head.

*****Divide into three**
Choose three strong singers to lead a group each. *Take the hat* is then sung as a round. (Group 2 starts from the beginning when group 1 reaches the second line and so on.) Stop when group 1 has sung all the way through twice.

*****Add more**
When the group is good at passing, add more of the same items e.g. six hats.

*****Three circles**
Divide into three groups and give a hat to each group, who pass the hat while singing.

***What is this?**
Hold up items of clothing and ask *"What is this?"*
Reply: *"It is a ..."*
Change leaders.

****Is this yours?**
As *What is this?* but the leader asks *"Is this yours?"*
Reply: *"No, it isn't mine!"* or *"Yes, it is mine!"*
Change leaders.

*****Take off your shoe!**
Sitting in a circle, everyone takes off one shoe and passes it, while singing *Take the shoe,* round the circle (on the beat).

sweatshirt socks vest shorts t - shirt skirt blouse tie

anorak glasses sunglasses mackintosh wellington boots slippers football kit

shirt pants knickers bra bikini swimsuit swimming trunks

What do you like for breakfast?

I like ...

*Sing and reply
Sing *What do you like for breakfast?*
Someone is chosen to reply
"I like ... for breakfast."
Everyone sings.

*What do you like to drink?
The leader asks,
"What do you like to drink?"
Reply: *"I like ... to drink."*
Change leaders.

*What do you like for lunch?
Ask everyone to make a list
of what they like to eat at
lunch time and ask in turn,
"What do you like for lunch?"
Reply: *"I like ... for lunch."*
Change leaders.

**Who likes ...?
Cut up magazines to
make flash cards for
different items of food
and drink. The leader holds
up a card and chants
"Who likes (chocolate cake)?"
Reply: *"I like (chocolate cake)"*
Leader: *"Who likes (sausages)?"*
Reply: *"I like (sausages)."*
and so on.

**Paper plates
Compare breakfasts
around the world. Make a list
of different countries and
their breakfasts. Using
a paper plate, or piece
of card cut to shape,
draw the different
breakfasts.

***List ten, name one
Ask everyone to write a list of
ten items of food that they like and
ten that they dislike. Ask each
person in turn to say
*"I like ... but
I don't like ..."*

***Breakfast conversation
Voice 1: *"Good morning!"*
Voice 2: *"Good morning!"*
Voice 1: *"Did you sleep well?"*
Voice 2: *"Yes, thank you."*
Voice 1: *"What would you like
for breakfast?"*
Voice 2: *"I don't know."*
Voice 1: *"Do you like cereal and
toast?"*
Voice 2: *"Yes please."*
Voice 1: *"What would you like
to drink?"*
Voice 2: *"I like orange juice,
please."*
Voice 1: *"Here you are."*
Voice 2: *"Thank you."*

My favourite food

40–43

2. My favourite food's vanilla ice cream.

3. My favourite food is strawb'ry ice cream.

How much is it, please?

*Listen and sing
Play or sing
My favourite food.
Everyone joins in. When the song is known well, someone is chosen to sing the solo.

*Change flavours
Add your favourite flavours to the song. There are some suggestions around the edge of the page.

*Draw ice cream cones
Draw a picture of your favourite ice cream cone to cut out and use for buying and selling!.

**My favourite flavour
Say *"My favourite flavour is chocolate ice cream.
What is yours?"* Reply: *"I like ... flavour ice cream."*

**Make money!
Place thin tracing paper over some coins and rub char-coal or pencil over them. These can then be cut out, backed with card and used to buy the ice creams!

***Buying and selling!
Work in pairs. One person is given the ice creams and one the money.
Voice 1: *"Hello"*
Voice 2: *"Hello, can I help you?"*
Voice 1: *"I would like a choco-late ice cream please."*
Voice 2: *"Here you are."*
Voice 1: *"What does it cost?"*
Voice 2: *"One pound fifty."*
Voice 1: *"Thank you!"*
Voice 2: *"Thank you!"*
Change over.

***Customer conversation
Choose two people to be the vendor and the customer at an ice cream van.

Voice 1: *"Good morning. Can I help you?"*
Voice 2: *"Yes please. I would like two ice creams."*
Voice 1: *"What flavour would you like?"*
Voice 2: *"I would like one choco-late and one strawberry. How much is it please?"*
Voice 1: *"£2 or 3 euros."*
Voice 2: *"Here you are."*
Voice 1: *"Thank you. Here are your ice creams."*
Voice 2: *"Thank you."*
Voice 1: *"Here is your change."*
Voice 2: *"Thank you."*
Voice 1: *"Goodbye!"*
Voice 2: *"Goodbye!"*

1 euro 90 cents   1 pound 20 pence   2 euros 36 cents   3 pounds 65 pence   4 euros 82

Where is the banana?

44–47

Sing this song in three stages:

*Behind your back
Sing the song.
Everyone joins in with
"Behind your back."

*Under the chair
As *Behind your back*
but this time the group
sings *"Under the chair."*
as well.

*Who put it there
This time everyone joins in
with *"who put it there?"*
as well, so that the song becomes
a question and answer game.

behind the ...   above the desk   on the table   under the chair   in the cup   in front of the ...

29

pepper   cucumber   lettuce   tomato   cauliflower   green pepper   cabbage   mushroom   onion   garlic   carrot   walnuts   potato

Under the chair

*Listen and mime
Everyone listens to
Where is the banana
then joins in miming
the actions.

*Two groups
When the song is well known,
sing like a question and
answer between
two groups

*Where is the banana?
Choose someone to
go out of the room while
a banana is hidden behind
another person's back.
Everyone shouts out,
"Where is the banana?"
Reply: "Behind ...'s back?"
Change over when the answer
is guessed correctly.

*What's behind my back?
Introduce other fruits
and vegetables. Put eight
items in a basket, then hide
one behind your back and say,
"What's behind my back?"
The first person to answer
correctly becomes the
new leader and so on.

*Pass the fruit
The leader says
"..., please pass
the (pear) to ..."
Change leaders.

**Fruit cup
Using different coloured
cups or mugs ask different
people to place different
fruits into the mugs. e.g.
"Elodie, please put the
plum into the white cup,"
or "Damien, please
put the lemon into
the red mug."
Change leaders.

**Where is the cabbage?
Place a cabbage in
different parts of the room
and ask "Where is the cabbage?"
Reply: "It is in front of
the computer." etc.
Change leaders.

***Market stall
Choose two people
to be the vendor and
the customer at a
market stall.
Voice 1: "Good morning. Can
I help you?"
Voice 2: "Yes please. I would
like two apples and
three pears."
Voice 1: "That is £1.56, please.
Anything else?"
Voice 2: "Four bananas please.
How much is it?"
Voice 1: "£2.43 all together."
Voice 2: "Here you are."
Voice 1: "Thank you. Here is
your change."
Voice 2: "Thank you, goodbye!"

apple   orange   banana   pear   plum   lemon   lime   peach   apricot   strawberry   raspberry

Animal rhythm

	clap	clap	clap	clap
Leader:	" lion"	All: " lion"		
	"tiger"	"tiger "		
	"alligator"	"alligator"		
	"hippo"	"hippo"		
	"kangaroo"	"kangaroo"		
	"crocodile"	"crocodile"		
	"elephant"	"elephant"		
	"zebra"	"zebra"		

*Keep a rhythm going
Start clapping.
Once the clapping is rhythmical the leader begins to chant *Animal rhythm* and every-one copies.

**Change action
Try a new action,
click, clap, tap, clap
(very slowly and rhythmically).
Click fingers, clap hands, tap table top, clap hands. Practise these actions before trying to say the animals too.

***Even harder
Try these actions with *Animal rhythm* before trying the *Zoo rap* below.
Slap, click, clap, slap
Slap your chest (or a table top), click fingers, clap hands and slap chest again.

Zoo rap

48-50

Slap   click   clap   slap   slap   click   clap   slap

Li - on,   ti - ger,   al - li - ga - tor,   hip - po,   kan - ga - roo.
Li - on,   ti - ger,   al - li - ga - tor,   hip - po,   cro - co - dile.

slap   click   clap   slap   slap   click   clap   slap

These   are   all   the   a - ni - mals   you'll   see   at   the   zoo.
These   are   all   the   a - ni - mals   that   will   make   you   smile.

**Chant
The leader chants *Zoo rap* and everyone joins in.

***Add new
At a later stage add new animals to the rap, as long as the words 'kangaroo' and 'crocodile' are kept.

I'm a very hungry alligator

2. I'm a very hungry great white shark, I'm waiting for my tea ...

3. I'm a very hungry lioness, I'm waiting for my tea ...

4. I'm a very hungry grizzly bear, I'm waiting for my tea ...

To do the penguin waddle

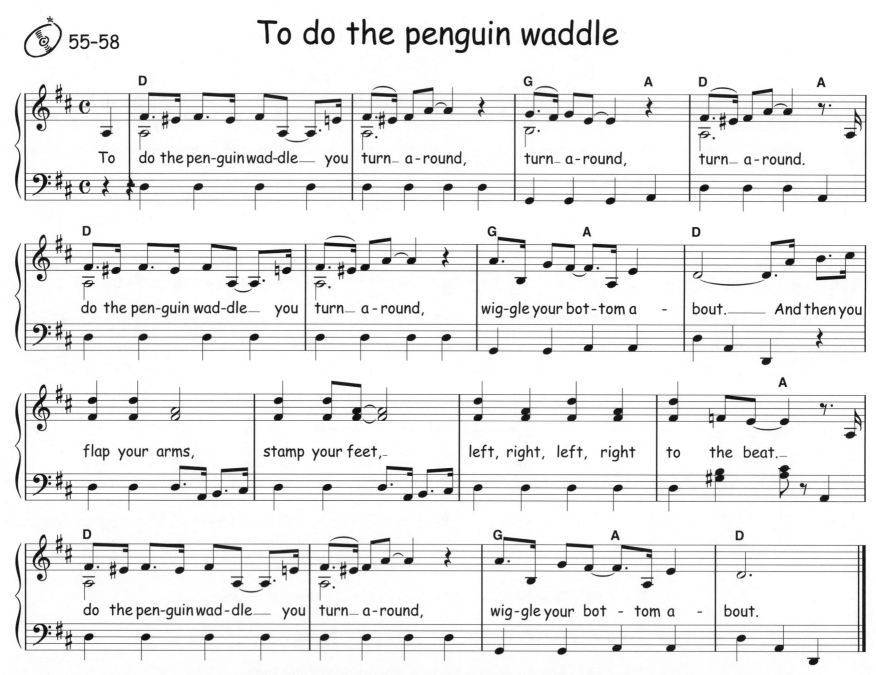

To do the Penguin waddle keep your knees together, feet apart and follow the song's instructions!

I am huge, I have a long nose, I am grey. What am I?   I am small, I like fish, I waddle. What am I?

33

Animal riddles

*Listen and sing
Play or sing
Penguin waddle
Everyone joins in.

**Add the actions
Stand in a long line facing the front with knees together and feet apart. Shuffle round to the right while singing the first four bars, then half way round to the left and wiggle your bottom. Jump to face the front again (still with knees together and feet apart), flap arms and stamp feet. For the last line of the song, turn to the right and face the back, wiggling bottoms. On the final note, everyone jumps to face the front.

**What am I?
Leader: *"I am small, I like fish, I waddle, what am I?"*
Reply: *"You are a ..."*

**Change leaders
Leader: *"I am tall, I have a long neck, what am I?"*
Reply: *"You are a ..."*

***Make more
Make up riddles like the ones round this page and say: *"I am ... what am I?"*
Reply: *"You are a ..."*

**Animal cards
Make two sets of animal cards, enough for everyone to have one. Give out the cards and ask, *"What is your animal?"* Reply: *"My animal is a ..."*

***Collect pairs
Give out two sets of animal cards. Choose (Jack) to say to (Lottie) *"Lottie, do you have an elephant?"* Lottie: *"I'm sorry Jack I don't"* or *"Yes Jack, I do."* Lottie then continues the game and so on until all the pairs are collected.

***Animal noises
Give everyone an animal card. Say to someone, *"What are you? Make a noise"*. That person makes an animal noise for everyone to guess and then says *"What am I?"*. He then becomes the new leader and so on.

What's your name?   How old is your brother?   How many uncles do you have?   Who is this?

34

Revision activities

Conversation for two

Rebecca: *"Hello!"*
Michael: *"Hi!"*
Rebecca: *"What's your name?"*
Michael: *"Michael. What's yours?"*
Rebecca: *"Rebecca"*
Michael: *"Very pleased to meet you."*
Rebecca: *"Very pleased to meet you."*

How many?

Hugh: *"How many uncles do you have?"*
Katy: *"I have two"*
Hugh: *"What are their names?"*
Katy: *"They are Robin and David."*
        "How many uncles do you have?"
Hugh: *"I don't have an uncle but I do have three aunts."*
Katy: *"What are their names?"*
Hugh: *"They are Jenny, Liz and Diana."*

Tom's family tree (page 11)

How old is Tom?
How old is Grandfather Smith?
How many cousins does Tom have?

Where do you live?

Emma: *"Where do you live?"*
Matthew: *"I live in a big town."*
Emma: *"Do you live in a house or a flat?"*
Matthew: *"I live in a flat with my grandmother."*
Emma: *"Is it big or small?"*
Matthew: *"It is small."*

Monster description

Ask someone to describe their monster:
*"This is my monster
His name is Pimple.
He has two small heads,
enormous noses and
purple eyes.
He has short legs and
long arms.
He is fat."*

Pass the bag

Hold up an item from a
bag of clothes and say,
"Is this a shirt (Sophie)".
Sophie: *"No, it's a dress"*
Pass the box to Ben who
continues the game.

At the zoo

Adam: *"I'm hungry"*
Lucy: *"Would you like a banana?"*
Adam: *"Yes please!*
Lucy: *"Let's go and see the elephants?"*
Adam: *"Can I feed them?"*
Lucy: *"No, but you can feed the giraffes.*
Adam: *"Good, let's go."*
Lucy: *"This way, follow me!"*

Make up more

Encourage your group
to make up conversations
in twos, threes or fours.

How many pets do you have?   Who lives in your house?   Who am I?

How do you like for breakfast/tea?   What do you like for breakfast/tea?   It is mine!   Whose is this?

guiro claves, saucepans, basket, wastepaper bucket, plastic - drums *(left margin)*

chime bars hand chimes - milk bottles xylophone glockenspiel bells *(right margin)*

Percussion ideas

Hello everybody
Everyone sits in a circle and is given an instrument. With very young children draw a chalk circle on the floor. They cannot reach over this to pick up instruments until you say. Create a question and answer percussion game. While saying *"hello everybody"* play four beats on the drum. Everyone echoes this with the same four beats.

Number 23
In a circle, each person plays their instrument in turn for four counts, e.g. on words *who, lives, my, house* etc. It is important to anticipate picking up the instruments to be ready to play. When good at this, choose one line for everyone to play together.

I have a mouth and nose
Choose people to play two different instruments, e.g. claves and rainstick. The claves on the words *"mouth and nose"* (1, 2, 3) and the rainstick on *"wiggle your eyebrows."*

Heads, bodies, legs
Give out 6 (tambourines) 5 (drums) 4 (claves) 3 (guiros) 2 (triangles) and 1 (cabaca) to play two bars of three beats in the appropriate place e.g. tambourines play on *"six for a body."* Alternatively try body percussion i.e. tapping the various parts of the body in time.

Monster stomp
Create a hi-hat backing by listening to the CD and creating sound effects to the rhythm *"monster stomp, the monster stomp, the"*. First get everyone to say the words over and over again (ostinato) to the CD then swap the words for *tss!* - keeping the same rhythm. Someone could try a cabaca or guiro. Play a big drum on the beat before each *"... stomp your feet"*. Also try walking around as you sing, stomping and stopping at the appropriate moment.

Take the hat
Change the words to *"take the (drum)"* etc. The last line becomes *"I can play the (drum)"*. Pass a drum on the 1st beat and play on 2, 3, 4. When good at this add a second drum.

Where is the banana
Use toy fruit shakers. On the word 'banana' the banana is thrown to the leader (who remains in control of the flying banana!) The leader passes it to a new person who hides it behind his back and shakes on the beat for the next verse.

I'm a very hungry alligator
Use this song as an assessment game. Have a circle of alligators with one person in the middle who can be eaten by the alligators. Ask a question at the end of each verse e.g. *"Am I playing a high or low note; fast or slow?"* etc. If the person in the middle gets it right he is saved, if not he is eaten. You will have lots of volunteers.

CD track list

	Track
Hello everybody	
Listen (Caroline, Ben, William, Friederike)	1
Join in (make 4 introductions)	2
How many sisters?	
Listen (Caroline)	3
Copy line by line	4
All the way through (3 verses)	5
On your own with the band (3 verses)	6
Draw your family tree!	
Listen (Caroline)	7
Copy line by line	8
All the way through (4 verses)	9
On your own with the band (4 verses)	10
Number 23	
Listen (Ben)	11
Copy line by line	12
All the way through (x 1)	13
On your own with the band (x 2)	14
Touch your elbow	
Listen (Ben)	15
Copy line by line	16
All the way through (x 2)	17
On your own with the band (x 2)	18
I have a mouth and nose	
Listen (Caroline)	19
Copy line by line	20
All the way through (4 verses)	21
On your own with the band (4 verses)	22
Heads, bodies, legs	
Listen (Caroline)	23
Copy line by line	24
All the way through (x 2)	25
On your own with the band (x 4)	26
Monster stomp	
Listen (Ben)	27
Join in and sing along	28
All the way through (4 verses)	29
On your own with the band (4 verses)	30

	Track
Take the hat	
Listen (Caroline)	31
Copy line by line	32
All the way through (x 1)	33
All the way through (as a round)	34
On your own with the band (1st voice x 2)	35
What do you like for breakfast?	
Listen (Caroline)	36
Copy line by line	37
All the way through (x 1)	38
On your own with the band (x 2)	39
My favourite food	
Listen (Caroline)	40
Copy line by line	41
All the way through (3 verses)	42
On your own with the band (3 verses)	43
Where is the banana?	
Listen (Caroline)	44
Copy line by line	45
All the way through (x 1)	46
On your own with the band (x 2)	47
Zoo rap	
Listen (Ben)	48
Copy line by line	49
On your own with the drums (x 1)	50
I'm a very hungry alligator	
Listen (Ben)	51
Copy line by line	52
All the way through (4 verses)	53
On your own with the band (4 verses)	54
To do the penguin waddle	
Listen (Ben)	55
Copy line by line	56
All the way through (x 1)	57
On your own with the band (x 2)	58

The band:
Sam Swallow (Piano)
Ben Lumsden (Bass guitar)
Louisian Huba (Drums)